Dedicated to…
The students who take a stand
The parents who hold their hand
The teachers who speak up loud
You should all be very proud!!!

-Stephanie

**www.mascotbooks.com**

*Frenemy Jane: The Sometimes Friend*

©2015 Stephanie Sorkin. All Rights Reserved. No part of this publication may be reproduced, stored in a retrieval system or transmitted in any form by any means electronic, mechanical, or photocopying, recording or otherwise without the permission of the author.

**For more information, please contact:**
Mascot Books
560 Herndon Parkway #120
Herndon, VA 20170
info@mascotbooks.com

Library of Congress Control Number: 2015901419

CPSIA Code: PRT0415A
ISBN-13: 9781620866634

Printed in the United States

# Frenemy Jane

## The Sometimes Friend

Written by
**Stephanie Sorkin**

Illustrated by
**Susan Robinson**

# A Note to Parents

Bully. It's a term that we hear all too often. While its meaning goes much deeper than a textbook definition, Webster's dictionary defines it as (noun) "One habitually cruel to others who are weaker" and (verb) "To frighten, hurt or threaten a smaller or weaker person".

Most associate bullying with physical force, such as hitting or emotional force such as teasing. Sometimes, no overt violence or words are involved. A mean stare, a sideways glance, purposely leaving a child out, or ignoring a child repeatedly are also forms of bullying.

Many have images of what a bully looks like, after all, in movies and cartoons they are usually bigger, stronger, and scarier. The truth is, those who bully come in all shapes and sizes.

I'm proud to donate a portion of the author proceeds from *Frenemy Jane* to PACER's National Bullying Prevention Center. For more information, please visit their website at www.pacer.org/bullying. With each book sold, we will be that much closer to preventing bullying through education and awareness.

I know this girl, I'll call her Frenemy Jane.
Maybe you know someone sort of the same?
I've known her forever
But now things feel strange.
She used to be nice–
BOY, have things changed.

On Monday, she hugged me when I got to school.
We skipped arm in arm.
I felt really cool.

On Tuesday, she laughed when I stained my new shirt.
Jane didn't care that my feelings were hurt.

On Wednesday, she asked if I wanted to play.
Jane left out the others and pulled me away.

On Thursday in art, Jane spilled paint on my work.
She didn't even say sorry.
She just posed with a smirk.

On Friday, Jane asked me to be on her team.
I wasn't sure what to do.
What if she's mean?

Thank goodness it's over!
The school week felt long.
I sat with my mom,
She could tell something's wrong.

"Sweetie," she asked, "is everything alright?"
I wasn't sure where to start, as she hugged me real tight.

I sat on my bed with my eyes staring down.
I wore less of a smile and more of a frown.

I told my mom the story from beginning to end.
I felt confused.
Was Jane really my friend?

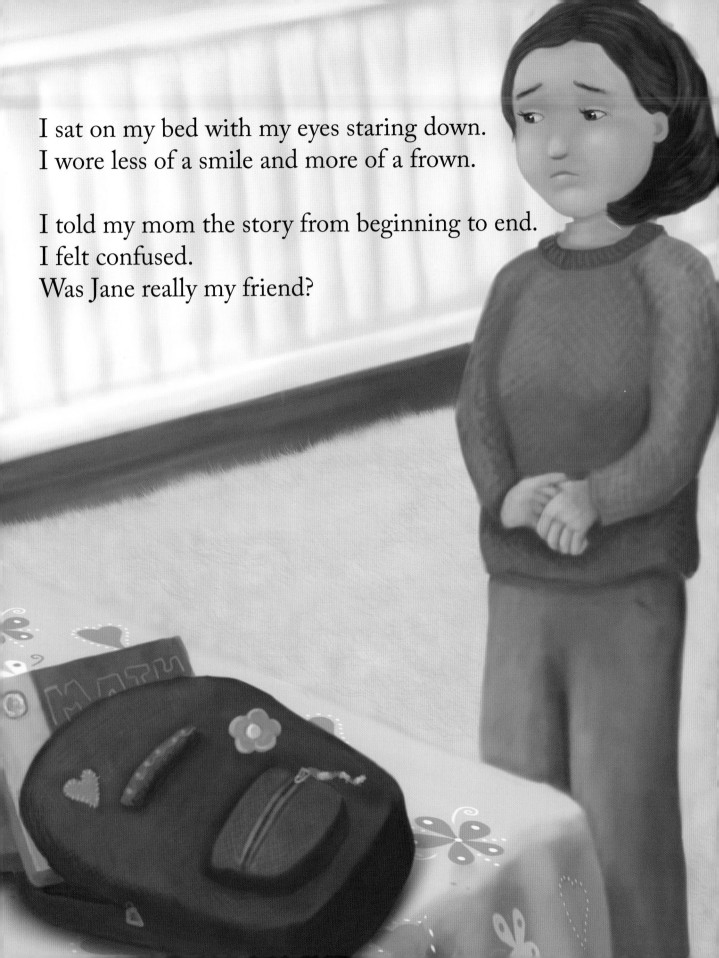

# GOOD

1 – Have known Jane since preschool

2 – She's sometimes funny

3 – Remembers my birthday

4 – Nice to me som

Mom told me to write a list,
The good things and bad.
When I'm with Jane do I smile?
Or do I always feel sad?

# BAD

1 - Laughs at me when something bad happens

2 - Wants me to be friends with only her

3 - Jane is mean to me

4 - Jane is mean to other people

- Jane leaves me and other kids out

"She's nice here and there, but not every day."
As I said it, I realized, this is NOT okay!
I suddenly felt better, safer, and stronger.
I didn't want to be pushed around any longer!

A "sometimes" friend, I'll call her.
For SOME this may be fine.
But a person like this
Is no friend of mine!

When kids have you feeling
Like you're riding a wave,
Day to day you don't know
Just how they'll behave!

It's Monday again.
This is going to be tough.
I'm standing up for myself today,
I've sat down long enough!

Do you have a "sometimes" friend?
What should you do?
Stand up or sit down?
It's all up to you!

Let's Talk About This...

# Classroom Discussion Questions

1. What did Jane do that made the main character, Maddie, feel badly?

2. What did Maddie do correctly in dealing with the way Jane was treating her? Was it right to tell her mom or was she being a "tattletale"?

3. Did Maddie do something to deserve bullying?

4. Was Jane being Maddie's friend?

5. Do you think that Jane was only mean to Maddie or do you think that she was mean to other kids too?

6. Can you bully someone without saying anything?

7. If your friend was being bullied by someone who was nice to you, what would you do?

8. Does bullying take place only at school?

9. What are some ideas you can use to deal with children who bully?

10. Can Maddie ever be Jane's friend again? What would Jane need to do to show that she can be trusted?

# Recipe
## Turn Your Frown Upside Down With
# Smiley Face Cupcakes

## Cupcakes
1 cup (2 sticks) of softened butter
1 cup sugar
2 cups flour
1 tsp baking powder
3 eggs
1 tsp vanilla extract

## For decorating
¼ cup jellybeans
¼ cup gummy worms
¼ cup small licorice pieces
¼ cup brightly-colored, sweetened cereal

1. Preheat oven to 350 degrees Fahrenheit.
2. Mix butter, vanilla extract, and eggs with an electric mixer.
3. Slowly add the dry ingredients: sugar, flour, and baking powder. Mix until smooth.
4. Pour mixture into baking cups.
5. Bake for 15-20 minutes.
6. Let cool for 15 minutes.

# Vanilla Frosting

4 cups confectioners sugar
4 tablespoons butter, softened
4 tablespoons milk
1 teaspoon vanilla extract
Food coloring (optional)

Combine sugar, butter, milk, and vanilla. Beat on medium speed until light and fluffy.

# Food Allergies?

The recipe can be easily adjusted to fit your needs!
- For gluten-free treats, use gluten-free flour.
- For an egg-free option, substitute the eggs with one 6-ounce container of Greek yogurt.
- For a dairy-free option, use Parve, non-dairy margarine in place of the butter. This recipe is peanut and tree-nut free, assuming that you check the manufacturing practices of all the ingredients.

# Short on time?

Use your favorite cake mix and prepare as per directions on the box.

# About the Author

Stephanie Sorkin lives in New York with her husband and three children. She is the author of the award-winning books *Nutley, the Nut-free Squirrel* and *Chocolate Shoes with Licorice Laces*. She is a member of the SCBWI and spends her time visiting schools to discuss the writing process and the joys of reading.

For more information, please visit her website at

# www.stephaniesorkin.com